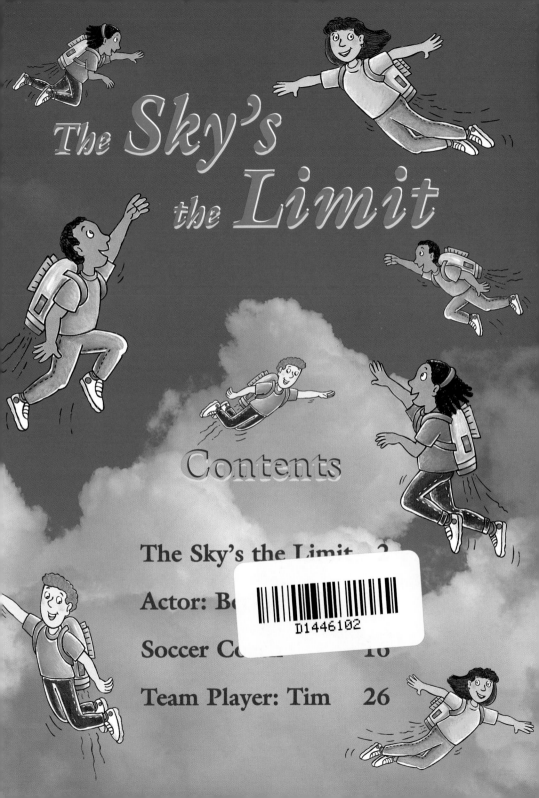

The Sky's the Limit

Contents

The Sky's the Limit

Written by Bob Eschenbach
Illustrated by Richard Hoit

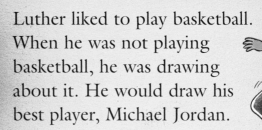

What do you think *the sky's the limit* means?

Luther liked to play basketball. When he was not playing basketball, he was drawing about it. He would draw his best player, Michael Jordan.

Luther was a whiz at drawing. He could think up all sorts of things about basketball in his mind and make them come to life on paper.

Luther did his best drawing at school. His art teacher taught him to add fine details to his pictures. Most of all, he taught Luther to try drawing all sorts of different things.

Luther would draw people from the past, like Hercules. He would draw his heroes, like Martin Luther King. Every day his drawings got better and better. His teachers said, "With Luther, the sky's the limit!"

One day, Luther and his parents were out in their car. They were hit by a truck that was following them. Luther was in the hospital for a long time. His legs were badly broken. The doctor had to put some pins in them to hold the bones together again. While he was in the hospital, he had lots of time to draw and lots of time to read. His mother and father brought his paper and his drawing pencils to the hospital for him. His art teacher came to visit to help him with new ideas for his drawings.

"Your legs will get better and you will be able to walk again," said the doctor. "But I think you will have to give up playing basketball. You will have to find something else to do."

"I can draw," said Luther, "but I can't draw all the time."

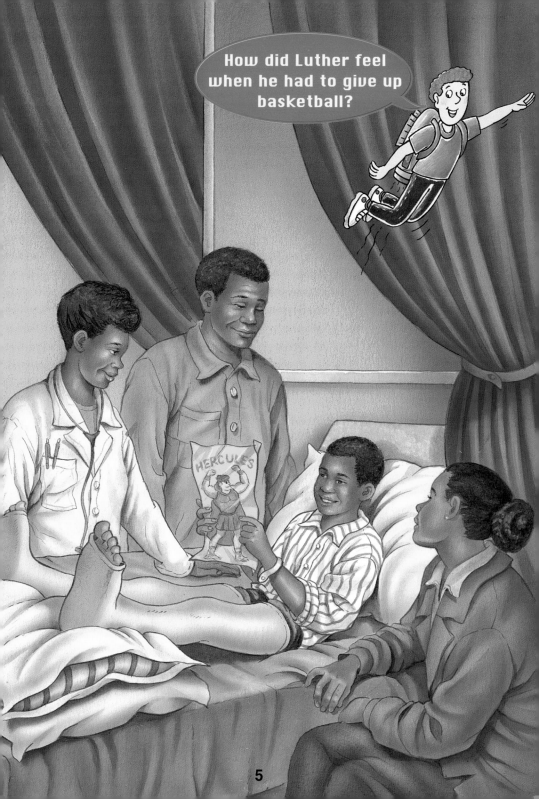

5

When Luther came home from the hospital, there was a big surprise waiting for him in his room. There, across from his table where he did his drawing, was a brand-new computer.

Soon, Luther didn't miss playing basketball at all. He would draw and read and use his computer at home. His mother showed him how to use the Internet to make new friends all around the world.

Every day, Luther logged onto the Internet. He wrote e-mail to people all around the world. They traded stories about families, school, and friends. But most of all, many of Luther's new computer friends wanted to know about his art. He was happy to scan his drawings into the computer and e-mail them to his friends across the other side of the world. Other people that Luther didn't even know asked him to send them his drawings, too.

One night, at dinner, Luther was telling his mother and father about the people who had asked him for his drawings over the Internet. "If people like your drawings so much, maybe you could start up a business on the Internet," said Luther's dad.

"You could put your drawings up for sale," said his mother.

"Wow!" said Luther. "That would be really good. Just think! I could show my drawings around the world and get paid for them!"

Do you know enough to do what Luther did?

When Luther told his art teacher at school about starting a business, he said, "The sky's the limit, Luther."

His art teacher helped Luther put his artwork into sets. There were sets of people, sets of heroes, sets of sports, sets of legends. Luther spent his time after school and on weekends getting his new business ready. He made more drawings to add to his sets. His mother showed him how to scan the sets of drawings one by one into the computer. He saved each set onto a floppy disk. Then he worked on fixing the tones and lines on each drawing with the computer's paint tool.

Now Luther's father showed Luther how to use the computer to make copies of each disk so that he would have them ready to sell. His father also showed him how to make his own website on the Internet. Luther put some of his drawings on the website along with all the things that people would want to know before they bought them. He also put an order form on the website for people to use.

Luther was pleased with what he had done. "I don't know if I would have set up a business on the Internet if my legs hadn't been broken," he said. "But, anyway, now I really know the sky's the limit!"

From Sharon Capobianco

Actor: Beckley

Beckley is an actor.
She is eighteen years old and
has been acting for eleven years.
We asked her to tell us about
her acting career.

Q When did you first think you would be an actor?

A I think I really always wanted to be an actor. My older brother Andy is an actor. We used to go and watch him. He looked like he was having fun up there on the stage. So one day I woke up and thought I would try it also.

Q How did you learn to act?

A I learned to act by watching all kinds of people. I tried to copy them. I watched how they talked and how they moved. Many times I would copy some of the people on the television. That helped me a lot.

Just being able to act does not make you a good actor. You also have to learn something called *stage presence*. You need stage presence as much as you need to be able to act. Your stage presence is what makes people look at you and listen to you.

Lots of things make up stage presence. How you hold your body, how you move on stage, how you speak, and how you sing are all parts of stage presence. Now that I know about stage presence, I look at other actors to see if I can see their stage presence.

Q What are some of the shows that you have been in?

A I have been in a lot of shows. When I was really young, I was in fairy tales. The first one I did was *Jack and the Beanstalk* and the second one was *Goldilocks and the Three Bears*. Later, when I was older, I played the princess in *Aladdin* and Beauty in *Beauty and the Beast*. Now I am playing in *Pocahontas*.

Q What is the hardest thing about acting?

A One of the hardest things to do is to keep being the person you are playing. This is called *staying in character*. This is really hard sometimes when something goes wrong on stage. If someone forgets their lines and you start cracking up, you would "break" character. Actors are not meant to forget their lines but sometimes it happens. When it happens, you have to make sure that you stay in character. That way the audience will not know that a line is forgotten because you are not showing it. The next thing to learn is how to *ad lib*. This means that you can make up a line to cover the one that someone forgot.

Q What do you like most about acting?

A I like acting in front of people and making them happy. When I look out at the people watching me act and I see them smiling, I feel good.

Q What do you not like about acting?

A I don't like rehearsing for a play. Rehearsing takes a long time because you have to go over and over it lots of times until all the actors get it right.

Q Have there ever been times that you would rather forget?

A Yes. One time I was playing in *Beauty and the Beast* and I had a bad cold. My voice was nearly gone. I went to sing a song and my voice sounded more like the Beast than Beauty.

Another time I was playing Pocahontas on an outdoor stage. It started to rain. The sidewalks were flooded. The next time I had to go on stage, I slipped on the wet sidewalk. My feet went up in front of me and I landed on my back.

The worst time of all was when I had to dance and sing in one show. As I danced, my skirt suddenly fell off. Everyone was laughing and I was trying to sing a love song. I just held my skirt around my waist as if nothing had happened. I almost gave up acting after that!

Q | What did you learn that helps you most with acting?

A | I think that learning to read plays has helped me the most. When we read plays at school, I learned about characters. I learned not only what the characters did but also what they were thinking about. If you are an actor who plays characters that lived in a different time, you have to read about that time so that you can get the character right. I learned that at school, too.

Were you right with your predictions?

Soccer Coach

Written by Sharon Capobianco
Illustrated by Marjorie Scott

Do you know the rules of soccer?

Jessica coaches soccer. She is sixteen years old. She has been playing soccer since she was six and coaching soccer since she was twelve. Jessica started by helping the coach with an indoor soccer team for young children. Now she is coaching a team of girls who are all under twelve.

Jessica likes coaching her soccer team. She says it is hard to say what she likes best about it. She always feels really good when she sees a smile spread across the face of one of the kids. She knows that she helped to put it there. To know that she is important to the players is important to Jessica, too.

Sometimes she gets a hug from one of the girls. Then Jessica has a smile from ear to ear.

It was not Jessica's idea to coach a soccer team. One year a team did not have a coach. A father, who had been asked to coach, asked Jessica if she would like to help him. Jessica said yes.

Jessica learned how to coach soccer by watching coaches who had coached her in the past. She learned from the good things that her coaches did and she learned, too, from the mistakes that they made. She also took a coaching course to make sure that she knew enough to be a coach.

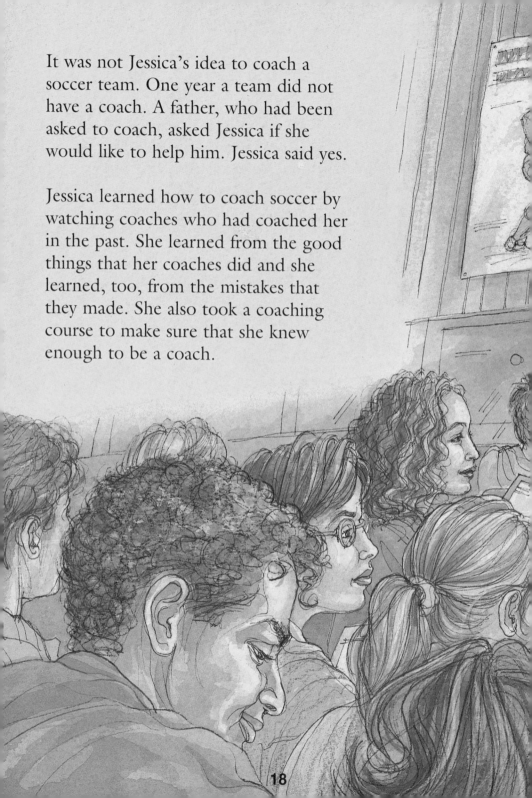

Jessica spends all her Saturdays at the soccer fields. She gets there in the morning and doesn't leave until all the games are over. She spends a lot of time talking with the players and teaching them all she can.

Jessica doesn't just teach her young players how to play soccer. She also teaches them about teamwork and supporting one another on and off the field. She teaches them about themselves and about life.

The girls also help Jessica learn more and more about herself. "In the beginning, I found I had to have lots of patience. I had to learn not to get mad with the players when they didn't do things just the way I wanted them to. I had to keep telling myself that they were only learning. I always put the players first. I give up my free time to coach soccer because this is what I like to do. I get just as much fun out of it as the girls do. Nothing makes me feel the same as when I am out there with my soccer team."

Jessica finds that coaching soccer has a downside, too.

"Often I have to talk to difficult parents. Because I am young, many parents try to tell me what to do. They try to tell me when we are going to train. They try to tell me how to run the soccer training sessions and how long they will be. I have to keep very calm and tell them that I'm the coach and I will decide how the training sessions will be.

"Another thing I don't like about coaching is the way I hear some parents yelling at their kids when they come to watch the game.

"These parents need to learn how to say something nice to their kids. They need to talk about the good things their kids are doing, not always the bad things."

22

There are lots of things Jessica has to figure out so that she can fit coaching soccer into her life.

She has to plan her time really well. She has to be able to fit in school, homework, sports, and her job as a referee, as well as coaching. She has to find times for training sessions that fit in with what she has to do and that also fit in with the team's schedules.

Jessica says that she would tell anyone who wanted to become a soccer coach that the kids are there to have fun. That is what it is all about. "You must try to answer their needs and teach them as much about both the sport and life as you can. Hang on to each smile and hug that they give you because it will mean more than any money ever will."

I hope to keep coaching soccer for as long as I can. One day, it may become my full-time career. *Jessica*

Team Player: Tim

Written by Denise Iversen

Tim had been very sick. He had been in
the hospital for four months. But now
he was ready to go back to school.
Because Tim had been really sick,
he had forgotten how to do many things.
He would have to learn how to do these
things all over again.

Do you know
what to do
to help someone
with epilepsy?

Tim's friends were all happy to see Tim back at school.

"We like it now you're back," said Jose. "But why are you wearing that funny hat?"

Tim put his head down so everyone could have a good look at his hat.

"I can tell you about Tim's funny hat," said Tim's mother. "It's a long story. You see, Tim has been sick for a long time now. While he was sick, some of his brain cells were damaged. Now he has epilepsy (epi lepsi)."

"What is epilepsy?" asked Katy.

"Epilepsy means that sometimes Tim's brain cells don't work evenly like yours do," said Tim's mother. "When Tim's brain cells don't work evenly, or blank out, he has what we call an epileptic seizure."

"What's an epileptic seizure?" asked Luke.

"If Tim has an epileptic seizure," said Tim's mother, "he will fall over and his body will shake and jerk. Every day, Tim takes pills to keep his brain cells from blanking out, but sometimes they are not enough to stop him from having a seizure. That's why he wears his funny hat. It will stop him from hurting his head when he falls."

"What should we do if Tim has a seizure?" asked Emma.

How would you help someone who is having a seizure?

"Keep cool. Don't be afraid," said Tim's mother. "Tim doesn't know he's having a seizure, so you can make sure that he won't hurt himself. Make sure that there is nothing in the way that he can fall on during the seizure. Wait for the seizure to stop. When Tim wakes up, he sometimes likes a drink of water or a short rest. Then he will be just the same as before."

"What other things can we do to help Tim?" asked Samuel.

"Tim can't remember all the things he used to know. He has forgotten some of the things he knew. When he tries to remember things, you could help him," said Tim's mother. "Sometimes he won't remember your name. You could tell him again. You could teach him how to use the computer again. You know how he loves the computer. Or you could draw some pictures with him. You know how he loves to draw."

"Will he ever get better?" asked Ish.

"As far as we know, Tim will always have epilepsy," said Tim's mother. "But we hope that he will be able to do all the things he wants to do. The doctors will try to give Tim the right number of pills so that he will not have epileptic seizures too often."

Twelve years later...

"It's good that you could come and work for us, Tim," said Tim's new boss.

What work would you like to do? What is the limit for you?

Tim's boss took Tim into a room so that he could meet the other people. Tim talked to them about himself and about his epilepsy.

"You may want to know why I wear this funny hat," he said.
"I wear it because I have epilepsy. If I have an epileptic seizure, I fall over and my body shakes and jerks. Every day I take pills to keep me from having a seizure, but sometimes the pills are not enough. That's why I wear my hat. It will stop me from hurting my head when I fall.

"If I have an epileptic seizure, don't worry! But you can help. You can make sure that there is nothing in the way that I can fall on during the seizure. Then just wait for the seizure to stop. When I wake up, I sometimes have a drink of water or a short rest. Then I will be just the same as before and will be back into my work."

Tim's new friends shook Tim's hand. "Come with us," they said. "We are pleased you are on our team. Let us show you your computer."

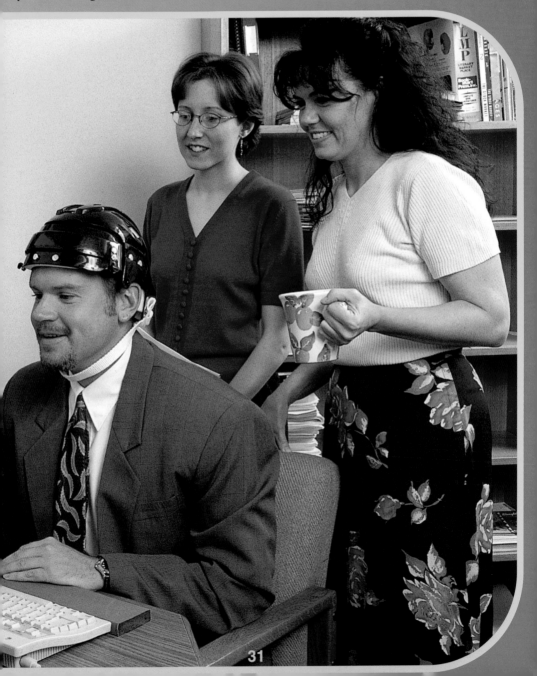

Glossary

ad-lib – to make up the words (or lines of a play) without any preparation

e-mail – mail that is sent from one computer to another computer

epilepsy – an "illness" that can bring about convulsions and a loss of consciousness

floppy disk – a small disk that stores information for computers

Internet – a network that links computers so that information and ideas can be shared

referee – a person who supervises a game or contest to make sure that the rules are followed

sidewalks (to a stage) – the approaches to the main stage at each side